STORY: MIKE PELLOWSKI ART: CHIC STONE & RUDY LAPICK LETTERING: BILL YOSHIDA
COLORING: BARRY GROSSMAN & NANCI TSETSEKAS
EDITORS: NANCI TSETSEKAS & VICTOR GORELICK EDITOR-IN-CHIEF: RICHARD GOLDWATER

ARCHIE'S DOUBLE DIGEST MAGAZINE (ISSN-87500671) No. 55 November 1991 Published 6 times a year in Jan. Mar., May July Sept and Nov. by Archie Comic Publications, Inc. 325 Fayette Avenue Mamaroneck, New York 10543 Richard H Goldwater President and Co-Publisher Michael I Silberkleit, Chairman and Co-Publisher ARCHIE characters created by John L Goldwater Single copies $2.25 in the U.S. $2.25 in Canada Subscription rate U.S $13.50 for 6 Issues, Canada, $13.50 All Canadian Postal Money Orders must be payable in U.S currency or by International Money Order All subscriptions include postage, handling and delivery right to your door 'Archie's Double Digest' and the individual characters names and likenesses are the exclusive trademarks of Archie Comic Publications, Inc Copyright © 1991, Archie Comic Publications, Inc. All rights reserved Nothing may be reprinted in whole or part without written permission from Archie Comic Publications, Inc This periodical may not be sold except by authorized dealers and is sold subject to the conditions that it shall not be sold or distributed with any part of its cover or markings removed, nor in a mutilated condition nor affixed to or as part of any advertising, literary or pictorial matter whatsoever No actual person is named or delineated in this fiction magazine and any similarities to real people and places in this fiction is purely coincidental Distributed in india by Variety Book Depot AVG Bhawan M-3 Con Circus P.O Box 505, New Delhi - 110001 India Second class postage rates paid at the post office at Mamaroneck, New York and at additional mailing offices Title registered in U.S Patent Office POSTMASTER send address changes to ARCHIE'S DOUBLE DIGEST co Archie Comic Publications Inc 325 Fayette Avenue Mamaroneck NY 10543

THE GREAT CAP'N CRUNCH CAPER

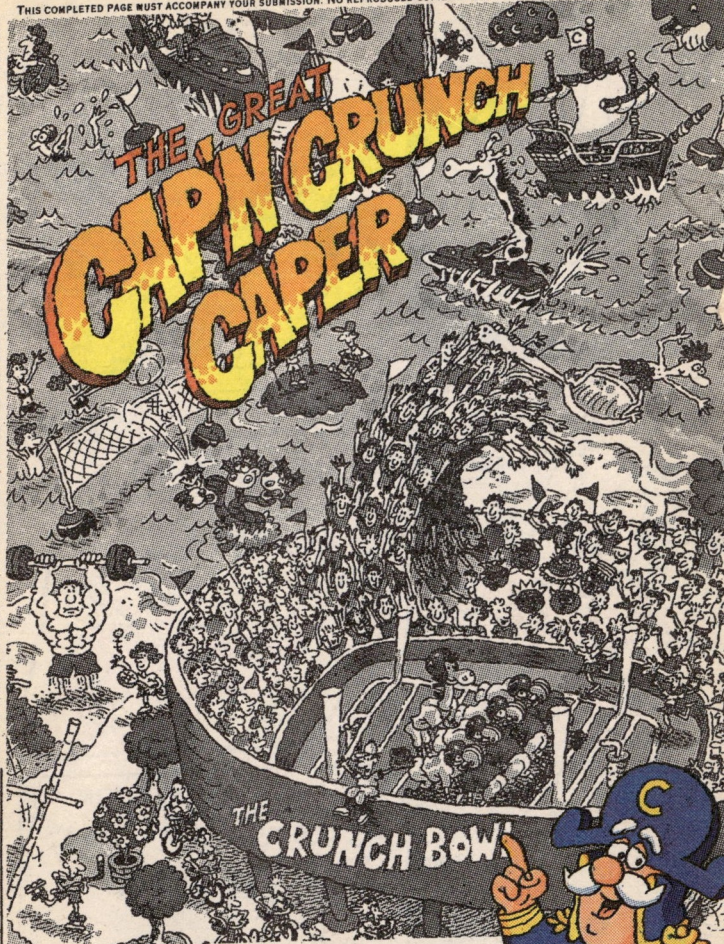

THE CRUNCH BOWL

"It's the Crunch Games. And if you can find the Crunchberries and their bush, the Peanut Butter Crunch Bird's egg and the Guppy, I'll send you a surprise!"

Just color them in and send this page to: Cap'n Crunch at the Guppy, P.O. Box 8230, Clinton, IA 52736. And send along your address and age so the Cap'n can track you down.

©1990 THE QUAKER OATS CO.

ATTENTION JUGHEAD FANS! DON'T MISS THESE TWO JUGHEAD TITLES: JUGHEAD WITH ARCHIE DIGEST MAGAZINE #107 (on sale September 3, 1991) AND JUGHEAD JONES DIGEST MAGAZINE #72 (on sale October 8, 1991).

?

WHAT HAPPENED TO YOU?

SOME MESS, EH, POP?

I WAS PAINTING A ROOM AT VERONICA'S HOUSE!

AT VERONICA'S HOUSE??

YOU'VE BEEN PAINTING AT *VERONICA'S* HOUSE?

I'VE BEEN AFTER YOU TO PAINT OUR HALL FOR OVER A YEAR!

GEE, POP! I'LL GET TO IT!

OH, I CAN GUARANTEE THAT! YOU'LL GET TO IT, ALL RIGHT!

RIGHT NOW!!

3

END

BOO!

BEWARE: Don't Let Other Kids Scare You Out Of Your Trading Card Treats.

TRADING CARDS DESIGNED ESPECIALLY FOR HALLOWEEN.

You've heard of card tricks. Now there are card treats. They're totally new this Halloween, and they come in all kinds of cool characters like Marvel Super Heroes,™ Archie® Comic characters, Official Universal Studios Monsters,™ Nintendo,® Inspector Gadget,™ and Widget.™ Look for Trading Card Treats™ wherever Halloween candy is sold. They're so much fun, it's scary. **From Impel Marketing Inc., produced in partnership with the National SAFE KIDS Campaign.**™

TRADING CARD TREATS National SAFE KIDS Campaign™

STATES OF MIND

Interesting facts about the States of the Union, based on their abbreviations!

The cleanest state--

WASH.

The most fatherly state--

PA.

The state with the most old maids--

MISS.

The unhealthiest state--

ILL.

The state with the most doctors--

MD.

The most personal state--

ME.

The state with the biggest mines--

ORE.

The state you can count on--

10

TENN.

The most musical state--

DO RE FA ME SO

LA.

GET A SEVEN-ISSUE SUBSCRIPTION
FOR ONLY $5.00! SAVE $2.00
ON EVERY SUBSCRIPTION
YOU ORDER! YOU'LL RECEIVE
THE NEXT SEVEN ISSUES AS THEY ARE
PUBLISHED!

POSTAGE
AND
HANDLING
PAID BY
ARCHIE!

DISCOUNT 32 PAGE COMIC SUBSCRIPTION!

ENCLOSE $5.00 FOR EACH
SUBSCRIPTION CHECKED ON
THE RIGHT AND MAIL IT TO

DISCOUNT
SUBSCRIPTION OFFER
c/o ARCHIE COMIC PUB., INC.
325 FAYETTE AVENUE
MAMARONECK, NY 10543

CHECK THE SUBSCRIPTIONS
YOU WANT BELOW!

OFFER EXPIRES NOVEMBER 30, 1991

NAME _____ _____
(PLEASE PRINT) FIRST   LAST

ADDRESS _____

AGE ___
☐ BOY
☐ GIRL

CITY & STATE _____ ZIP ___

OFFER AVAILABLE IN U.S. AND CANADA ONLY
PLEASE NOTE: ALL CANADIAN ORDERS MUST BE PAYABLE IN U.S. CURRENCY,
OR BY INTERNATIONAL MONEY ORDER. PLEASE ALLOW 8 TO 10 WEEKS DELIVERY.

ARCHIE	$5.00
BETTY AND ME	$5.00
BETTY AND VERONICA	$5.00
JUGHEAD	$5.00
VERONICA	$5.00
TEENAGE MUTANT NINJA TURTLES	$5.00
TOTAL AMOUNT ENCLOSED:	$ ___

459 / 459D

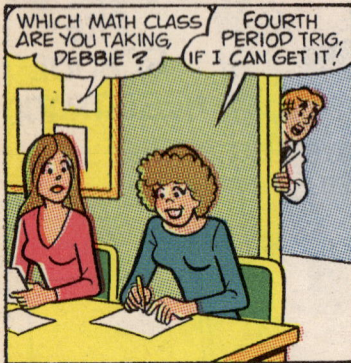

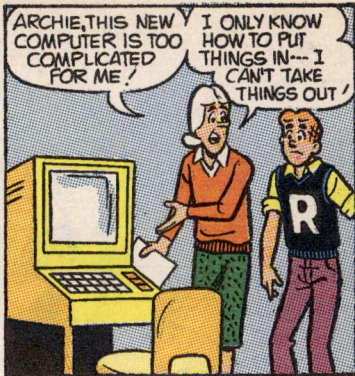

FIND OUT HOW LITTLE ARCHIE *IS SAVING THE PLANET!* DON'T MISS THIS ISSUE OF LITTLE ARCHIE DIGEST MAGAZINE #3 (on sale September 3, 1991).

ZOOM!

EEP!

WHEW! THAT WAS CLOSE! ALMOST DROPPED IT ON THAT FAT GUY!

MR. WEATHERBEE! YOU DID IT AGAIN! YOU SAVED MY LIFE AGAIN!! EVEN MY OWN DAD NEVER SAVED MY LIFE TWICE IN ONE DAY!

8

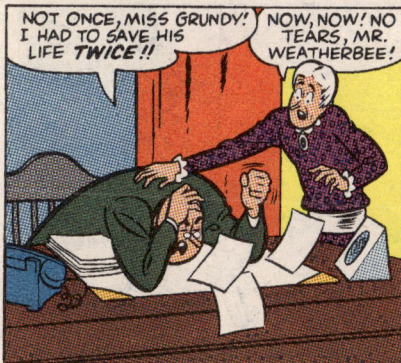

EVEN THE BAD GUYS LOOK UP TO HIM.

Where you gonna hide from a guy like Spider-Man®? He's on your left. He's on your right. He's on the wall. He's on the ceiling. And now, he's on Genesis.™

He probably won't be too happy about this mess. As if one enemy wasn't enough, this game's got all the big uglies, Dr. Octopus, The Hobgoblin, Venom, Electro, The Lizard, and The Sandman. Not to mention Kingpin running the show.

But Spidey's not exactly defenseless. Those bad guys won't look so bad when Spider-Man® starts laying into them with devastating kicks as he flies off the end of his web swing. And riffraff beware of his bone-crushing punches. If there's anything left, he'll wrap it up neatly with a barrage of web bolts.

Messing with Spider-Man® could be hazardous to your health. You've got to admit, he's one of the toughest American heroes ever. After this game, we know a couple of bad guys who probably would agree.

Leading the 16-bit revolution.

UH, OH! *TROUBLE!*

EH-HI, REG!

HI, JUG!

?

HEY!—DIDN'T YOU NOTICE ANYTHING STRANGE ABOUT MY FRIEND?

LIKE *WHAT?*

THOSE CRAZY EYES, THE BIG EARS, THE POINTY HEAD, THOSE WILD RAGS?

I FIGURED HE WAS YOUR *COUSIN* OR SOMETHING! HE CERTAINLY LOOKS *KOOKIE* ENOUGH!

HEY!—LOOK AT THAT WEIRD-LOOKING CHARACTER!

OOPS!—THEY'VE *SPOTTED* YOU!

SHUCKS, JIMMIE! THAT'S ONLY OL' JUGHEAD!

OH!

3

THESE ARE GIRLS! —FEMALES!

OH!—WE CALL THEM BLIPS!

"BLIPS?"—YOK! I COULDN'T HAVE PUT IT BETTER MYSELF!

KNOCK IT OFF, JUG!

THIS ONE WITH THE RED ROOF IS MUCH BLOONG!

HUH?

"BLOONG!" EH—IN YOUR TONGUE IT MEANS "CUTE!"

SHE'S PRETTY BLOONG HERSELF!

WHACK!

OUCH!

HEY! WHY DID SHE DO THAT?

THAT'S HOW WE EXPRESS AFFECTION ON THE PLANET NAUSEA!

2

OH, NO! NO, NO, NO! NOT THAT AGAIN! NO!
Jughead
DIG WE MUST
YOU'VE GOTTEN HOLD OF ANOTHER TREASURE MAP, GIVEN TO YOU ON HIS DEATHBED, BY A GRIZZLED OLD SEA CAPTAIN WHOM YOU BEFRIENDED!

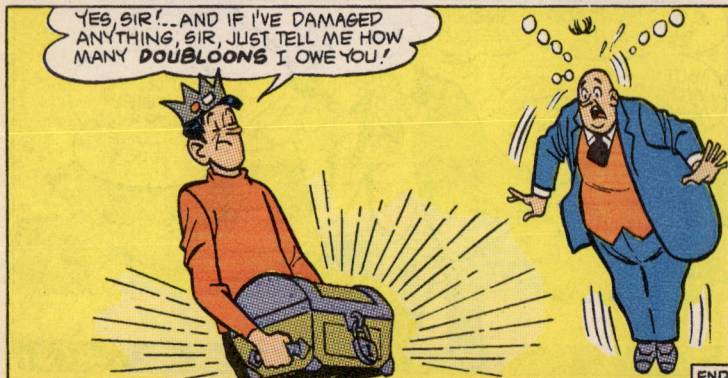

Archie *AND THE GANG* ¨RACE PACE¨

ARCHIE! THEY'RE HAVING A *VICTORY DANCE* AFTER THE MARATHON! LET'S YOU AND I GO TOGETHER!

OH, NO YOU WON'T!

RIVERDALE MARATHON STARTING LINE

I ASKED ARCHIE *FIRST!*

AND I ASKED HIM *LAST!*

JUG, WOULD YOU BELIEVE THIS? THE GIRLS ARE FIGHTING OVER *POOR L'IL ME!*

— ORDER FORM —

SIX-ISSUE DOUBLE DIGEST SUBSCRIPTION

ENCLOSED IS $10.00 FOR EACH TITLE CHECKED.

☐ JUGHEAD'S DOUBLE DIGEST MAGAZINE

☐ BETTY AND VERONICA DOUBLE DIGEST MAGAZINE

☐ ARCHIE'S DOUBLE DIGEST MAGAZINE

Number of Subscriptions Checked	TOTAL AMOUNT
_____ × $10 = $_____	

FIVE-ISSUE DIGEST SUBSCRIPTION

ENCLOSED IS $5.00 FOR EACH TITLE CHECKED.

☐ THE NEW LITTLE ARCHIE DIGEST MAGAZINE

☐ ARCHIE DIGEST MAGAZINE

☐ LAUGH DIGEST MAGAZINE

☐ ARCHIE ANDREWS WHERE ARE YOU DIGEST MAGAZINE

☐ JUGHEAD JONES DIGEST MAGAZINE

☐ JUGHEAD WITH ARCHIE DIGEST MAGAZINE

☐ BETTY AND VERONICA DIGEST MAGAZINE

☐ ARCHIE'S STORY & GAME DIGEST MAGAZINE

Number of Subscriptions Checked

☐ × $5 TOTAL AMOUNT $_____

MAIL TO:

ARCHIE'S SPECIAL DIGEST SUBSCRIPTION OFFER

c/o ARCHIE COMIC PUBLICATIONS, INC.
325 FAYETTE AVE., MAMARONECK, NY 10543

AVAILABLE IN U.S. AND CANADA ONLY OFFER EXPIRES NOVEMBER 30, 1991

NAME (Please print)   FIRST   LAST   AGE _____ GIRL ☐ BOY ☐

ADDRESS

CITY   STATE   ZIP

AMOUNT ENCLOSED FOR **DOUBLE DIGEST** SUBSCRIPTIONS ($10.00 EA. SUB.)	AMOUNT ENCLOSED FOR **SPECIAL DIGEST OFFER** SUBSCRIPTIONS ($5.00 EA. SUB.)	**TOTAL AMOUNT ENCLOSED:** (ADD ALL ORDERS)
$____	+ $____	= $____

PLEASE NOTE: ALL ORDERS MUST BE MADE PAYABLE IN U.S. CURRENCY OR BY INTERNATIONAL MONEY ORDER. PLEASE ALLOW 8–12 WEEKS FOR DELIVERY.

461D

VERONICA FINDS MORE THAN SHE CAN HANDLE WHILE SCUBA DIVING IN THE BAHAMAS!
DIVE INTO THE ADVENTURE OF VERONICA #18 (on sale October 8, 1991).

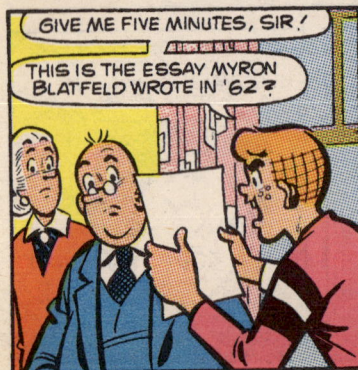

Jughead
IN
THE DISH
JUGHEAD, WHERE HAVE YOU BEEN ALL AFTERNOON ?
I WENT TO A NEW SPOT ON THE OTHER SIDE OF TOWN!
AND WHAT A DISH THEY HAD THERE!
I NEVER SAW ANYTHING PUT TOGETHER LIKE THAT!
JUGHEAD, THAT'S NO WAY TO TALK ABOUT A GIRL!
WHAT GIRL ?
IT WAS THE BIGGEST HAMBURGER I EVER SAW IN MY LIFE!
I SHOULD HAVE GUESSED THAT!
SLURP
THE END

MR. LODGE in "ANGLE WRANGLE"

DADDY, THE GANG WOULD LIKE TO USE OUR *INDOOR POOL!*

NO!

I GUESS WE'LL JUST HAVE TO ENTERTAIN OURSELVES!

YES!

ALL RIGHT, GANG! TAKE OUT YOUR INSTRUMENTS! WE'LL HAVE A *LITTLE ROCKSESSION!*

WHAT ??!!

The Archies

ER...MAYBE I WAS A LITTLE HASTY!

HMPF! TALK ABOUT ARM-TWISTING...

The End

IT'S Archie's 50th ANNIVERSARY FAN CLUB OFFER!

HELP CELEBRATE ARCHIE'S 50th ANNIVERSARY! JOIN THE ALL-NEW ARCHIE'S 50th ANNIVERSARY FAN CLUB AND RECEIVE A SPECIAL, LIMITED EDITION MEMBERSHIP CARD, FULL-COLOR BUTTON, 25 SHEET NOTEPAD AND A PEN THAT WRITES IN 3 COLORS! YOU'LL ALSO RECEIVE SPECIAL DISCOUNT COUPONS FOR OTHER GREAT ARCHIE PRODUCTS!

Tri-color pen

Archie 50 ANNIVERSARY SINCE 1941

25 page notepad

membership card

OFFICIAL MEMBERSHIP CARD
ARCHIE 50 CLUB ANNIVERSARY

This is to certify that
...is a member in good standing of Archie Club and is entitled to all the rights and privileges of membership in that fun-age news and Archie group of comic magazines.

full-color button

ALL FOR ONLY $5.00

ARCHIE'S
50th ANNIVERSARY FAN CLUB OFFER
c/o ARCHIE COMIC PUBLICATIONS
325 FAYETTE AVENUE
MAMARONECK, NEW YORK 10543

Total amount enclosed	Send me
$_____	_____ Kit(s)

☐ **YES!** ENROLL ME IN ARCHIE'S 50TH ANNIVERSARY FAN CLUB! ENCLOSED IS $5.00 FOR EACH MEMBERSHIP KIT ORDERED.

OFFER EXPIRES DECEMBER 31, 1991

OFFER AVAILABLE
I N U.S. AND CANADA ONLY

NAME _____ AGE _____ ☐ BOY
(PLEASE PRINT) FIRST   LAST   ☐ GIRL

ADDRESS _____

CITY & STATE _____ ZIP _____

PLEASE NOTE: ALL CANADIAN ORDERS MUST BE PAYABLE IN U.S. CURRENCY, OR BY INTERNATIONAL MONEY ORDER. PLEASE ALLOW 8 – 10 WEEKS FOR DELIVERY.

463D

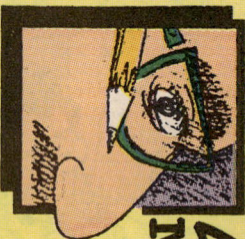

Editor's NOTEBOOK

Dear Archie Readers:

For those of you who are avid comic book collectors and those of you who aren't, here's a bit of information that may (or may not) surprise you.

Issue #21 of THE OFFICIAL OVERSTREET COMIC BOOK PRICE GUIDE lists *Archie #1, published in 1942, for $4,000 in mint condition.*

"$4,000!" you say. "I can't afford that, no way! Now I'll never get to see Archie #1!" Then I say, "Wrongo, you crazy comic collector! Listen to this!..."

You can enjoy exact reproductions of Classic Golden Age Archie Comics from the 1940's and also the 1950's in your school library or at home. Micro-Color International has reproduced these comics on Microfiche (mini film strips) which you can insert into, a Micro-Color projector. You can view every page, including covers and advertisements exactly as they appeared in Archie Comics during the 40's and 50's. If your library does not have a Micro-Color system, you can write for more information to:

MICRO-COLOR INTERNATIONAL,
85 Godwin Avenue,
Midland Park, NJ
07432

Send your cards and letters to:
Victor Gorelick, Editor,
ARCHIE COMIC PUBLICATIONS, INC.,
325 FAYETTE AVE., MAMARONECK, NY 10543.

Archie PRESENTS PREVIEWS!

A LOOK AT THIS MONTH'S SPECIAL ISSUES....

BETTY & ME #195
ON SALE AUGUST 27, 1991

HOLEY MOLEY! Awesome Archie entertainment does it again! Your favorite teen queen supreme gets her dream on a day when **EVERYTHING** goes wrong! Find out her secret! It could be the nicest thing you do for yourself this month!

BETTY & VERONICA #45
ON SALE AUGUST 27, 1991
LIGHTS, CAMERA, ACTION!

and Veronica are the stars of their own talk show! They get paid to do what they do best, **GOSSIP!** But they blab some secrets about their pals. Now who's seeing stars?! Read "Seeing Cable TV Stars" in this issue!

Li'l Jinx "SEE SAW"

Panel 1:
LI'L JINX---DID YOU SEE MY GOLF CLUB?

YES, DADDY--

Panel 2:
I SAWED IT IN THE GARAGE!

Panel 3:
NO! NO! YOU MEAN YOU SAW IT IN THE GARAGE!

Panel 4:
OR YOU COULD SAY, I HAVE SEEN IT IN THE GARAGE!

Panel 5:
OKAY! HAVE IT YOUR WAY, DADDY! BUT I STILL SAWED IT IN THE GARAGE!

END

SPLINTER AND THE TURTLES® ARE OUT TO STOP AN ALIEN CREATURE CALLED THE KEEPER WHO IS ABDUCTING MYTHOLOGICAL CREATURES! *FIND OUT WHAT HAPPENS IN TEENAGE MUTANT NINJA TURTLES*® #26 (on sale September 3, 1991)!

JUGHEAD

THE SOUND OF MUSIC

CONTINUED

R-R-RING!

R-R-RING!

REUSE PAPER!

Archie's ENVIRONMENTAL TIP

7

FUN FACTS

Reuse WHERE YOU CAN!! ☆ USE **BOTH** SIDES OF A SHEET OF PAPER! ☆ MAKE **WRAPPING PAPER** OUT OF OLD GROCERY BAGS OR SUNDAY COMIC PAGES! ☆ MAKE YOUR OWN **STATIONERY** FROM SCRAP PIECES OF PAPER! *HAVE FUN WHILE SAVING OUR NATURAL RESOURCES!*

☆ **BOWS** CAN BE MADE BY CUTTING SCRAP PAPER INTO STRIPS AND TAPING THEM TOGETHER!!

☆ AMERICANS RECYCLE ABOUT 27% OF THEIR NEWSPAPERS! * *-- NICE GOING, FOLKS!*

SEND YOUR IDEAS FOR SAVING AND REUSING PAPER TO:
DONNA BLOCK
℅ ARCHIE COMIC PUBLICATIONS, INC.
325 FAYETTE AVENUE,
MAMARONECK, NY 10543

* FROM THE RECYCLER'S HANDBOOK, PUBLISHED BY EARTHWORKS PRESS, BERKELEY, CA.

A PUBLIC SERVICE MESSAGE FROM **Archie** COMICS

DON'T MISS A SINGLE ISSUE
OF THIS GREAT FOUR ISSUE MINI-SERIES!
COLLECT `EM AND SAVE`EM!

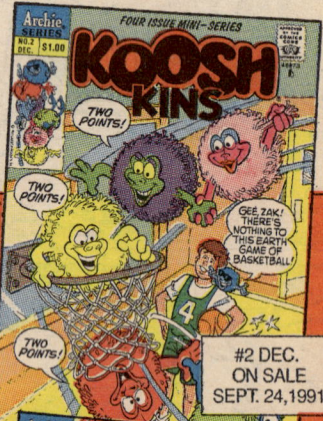

Brought to you by

Archie Comic Publications Inc.